The Martin G. Brumbaugh
Lectures in Education

The Martin G. Brumbaugh Lectures in Education were begun in the Summer of 1956 to provide an opportunity for the general public and the educators of the greater Philadelphia area to join the students at the University of Pennsylvania in hearing lectures by distinguished scholars who represent some of the academic disciplines which form the foundation for current American educational theory and practice. The lectures in the first series were:

"The Instrument Maker," Thomas Woody, *University of Pennsylvania*

"A Psychological Basis for Learning," J. W. Tilton, *Yale University*

"Dimensions of Social Stratification," August B. Hollingshead, *Yale University*

"Building a Philosophy of Education," J. Donald Butler, *Princeton Theological Seminary*

These addresses were subsequently published by the University of Pennsylvania Press under the title, *Foundations of Education.*

The present volume, *The Emergence of the Modern Mind,* makes the second series of addresses available to the general public.

Thanks is hereby given to authors and publishers for permission to quote from their published works and to all who have contributed to the success of the series.

Martin G. Brumbaugh, 1862–1930, was the first professor of pedagogy at the University of Pennsylvania, occupying the chair from 1895 to 1905. Subsequently, he rendered distinguished service as Commissioner of Education in Puerto Rico under President McKinley, as Governor of the Commonwealth of Pennsylvania, and as President of Juniata College.

CONTENTS

THE EMERGENCE
OF THE MODERN MIND

Our Biological Inheritance

CONWAY ZIRKLE

At the very beginning, I want to emphasize the fact that this talk is one in a series of talks, and that its title "Our biological inheritance" is really a sub-title. This morning we will deal with only one aspect of the general subject of the Brumbaugh Lectures of 1957, which is "The Emergence of the Modern Mind"; and we will consider our biological inheritance only as it applies to this more inclusive topic. Without this limitation, a subject such as this could be treated adequately only by a long and concentrated course in human genetics and, today, such a course would have to include medical genetics with some time devoted to the effects of radiation on our genes, and what this will do to the future of our species. We shall concern ourselves here however, with our biological inheritance only as it bears upon the origin, working, and probable fate of what is called "The Modern Mind." We shall consider our biological inheritance only as it helps us explain how we got this way, what is happening to us, and where we shall go from here.

Our biological background is important to us in many ways. We are—all of us—biological specimens and, no matter what else we may be in addition and no matter what great things we may accomplish, we shall remain biological specimens, that is, we are and shall remain animals. As long as we breathe, eat, and reproduce ourselves biologically, we shall have both the privileges and the limitations of citizenship in the animal kingdom.

At this point I would like to remove, if possible, some of the misconceptions that distort so much of our popular thinking. We have grown so accustomed to contrasting the human kind with the rest of the animal kingdom that we are more conscious of the differences than of the resemblances between ourselves and our fellow creatures. A startling example of this occurred at the Scopes trial in 1925, when William Jennings Bryan denied that man is a mammal, but this was before we had our modern styles of clothing. We use such adjectives as "humane" and "virtuous" which we derive from our unique status as human beings, and contrast them with adjectives like "bestial" and "brutal" which we derive from the rest of the animal kingdom. But this is only an instance of our parochial "species Chauvinism," and it overlooks the fact that *Homo sapiens* can be and has been far more brutal and bestial than any other mammal.

Once we recognize the fact that we are animals, we may observe ourselves with some perspective and even with a little objectivity. The animal kingdom is really not a bad place. It can be credited with, among other things, all human accomplishments—with our own achievements as well as with those of the other species. Human beings have really added quite a bit to this kingdom, for example, an animal named Ludwig von Beethoven composed nine symphonies of merit, and another one named Isaac Newton formulated the law of gravitation.

Indeed, the animals, who evolved on our small planet, have much to be proud of. Some species have evolved great our civilizations as an incidental result of the cooperative and cumulative activities of the extreme Mendelian segregants—activities that have extended over the ages. The result is that human beings are subjected to many strains and stresses that sometimes break through to the surface. Any dominant philosophy that disregards this underlying maladjustment does so at its peril. Philosophies that ignore this factor are soon discarded—sometimes violently. From the very beginnings of history, all world-views have been threatened by the fact that our species is not completely adapted to living in any civilized environment, and are even less adapted to the sometimes rapid changes caused by their maladjustment. Even the most modern minds—the most up-to-date ideologies—have often been engulfed in our periodic disorders called revolutions, and even our most idealistic and humanitarian doctrines have been destroyed, frequently by the very institutions they have helped to create.

The thoughts that may churn up at any time in the minds of the norm of our species are a limiting factor to all popular philosophies—to all modern minds. Sometimes those men, who are skilled in arousing these primitive responses, use their talents for their personal gain, and sometimes they acquire sufficient power to alter history. Many times such men have seized a nation or a culture and, through exercising social control and censorship, have determined what type of thinking shall be the mode. In some countries, a modern mind may, at times, be no more than the personal philosophy of a dictator. We should remember that Hitler and Stalin are not very far behind us, and that now the whole world awaits the outcome of a cold war, which is also a war of ideas, fought by propaganda. In some parts of the world, differences of opinion or conflicts of interests form excellent excuses for escaping the unnatural inhibitions of a civilization to which the inhabitants are incompletely adapted. To cite one example, massacres are now going along gaily in North Africa.

As these lines are written, the newspapers have just published a dispatch from Communist China. Mao, the present dictator, has stated openly that eight hundred thousand reactionary Chinese were killed for resisting conversion to what is now the modern mind in China. But Mao stated further that, at present and in the future, Communism will spread itself by more subtle means.

Our recent and our present troubles, however, do not necessarily indicate that our biological equipment is deteriorating, although we have other evidence that indicates that it probably does deteriorate very slowly in all civilized cultures. We are probably still very like our not-too-distant ancestors. We can take what comfort we can from the fact that, many times in the past, our ancestors have been no better than we are now, that they have many times equalled us at our worst, yet the human race still survives. It is true that today, we have many things that we would rather not think about, such things, for example, as our various kinds of terrorism—the red terror, the black terror, the white terror, etc.—but a century and a half ago there was the Reign of Terror in Paris. In the preceding centuries, ideas as goofy as any of ours have frequently dominated society. We need mention only the Children's Crusade, when the idea seems to have been that the Tomb of Our Blessed Savior could be rescued from the vile Infidel by Crusaders who scorned the use of force and who were going to rescue the Tomb solely by their overwhelming moral superiority.

In the sixteenth and seventeenth centuries, we had the religious wars when Catholics and Protestants killed each other with great enthusiasm and, on special occasions, burned each other at the stake. Then, too, there were the centuries of the witchcraft delusion, and the witches, when properly treated, confessed to their dealings with the Devil as routinely as present day Communists, in the losing cliques, confess to dealings with Capitalists. We still belong to the same old human race. Our biological heredity changes slowly in terms of our successive fashions in thinking, no matter how extremely rapidly it may change in terms of our organic evolution. In a half million years or so, we know humanity will be quite different—perhaps it may even be improved.

As stated earlier, this pseudo-constancy in our biological heredity enables us to evaluate the limits it puts on all of our intellectual conventions. It insures that our culture can never depart from the biological limitations of the cultured. Moreover, the fact that civilization has imposed on us standards of living and standards of conduct, to which we are imperfectly adapted, has produced tensions within us that sometimes express themselves in disconcerting ways. Every now and then society may have an attack of anti-intellectualism, or it may acquire a sudden enthusiasm for something or other; or, as our scientific knowledge becomes too esoteric for the laity, society may simply become confused. The Modern Mind may be at odds with itself over purely technical items such as fluorides in the drinking water, or strontium-90 in the topsoil. We have no simple or easy techniques for settling rationally such disputes when they arise, and we are faced with the constant threat of having to settle complicated matters by means of a majority vote. Thus almost any plausible notion may become one of the eternal verities for a generation or so, and almost any intellectual stance may be the mode for a day.

But over and beyond all these nuisances, we are faced with one fundamental biological limitation to our brain power—a limitation that promises to present a real danger to our species. This danger is inherent in the fact that the sum total of all our knowledge has become too much for us—too much even for the finest brains of our extreme Mendelian segregants.

The recent and enormous growth of our scientific information has brought new problems and dangers. Our total knowledge is now practically out of control: it has grown to a point where no single person can grasp it. In order to handle it at all, we have had to divide it up—to fragment it into specialties—and the best of us are competent in no more than one or two of these specialized splinters. This, of course, is no real solution, it is just the only one we have. But to achieve even the limited competence of specialists, we have to acquiesce in a superficial acquaintance with— sometimes even a total ignorance of—the other splinters of learning. As a result, we, as individuals, absorb misinformation easily and our culture as a whole suffers. Our culture can be easily infected in the cracks between the specialties as well as in those complex fields where the pertinent facts are scattered in the minds of different specialists. Thus, it is not remarkable that quackeries thrive among us, and at times, even limit the spread of knowledge from one scholarly field to another. We should never delude ourselves into believing that our own modern mind is free from these generally accepted quackeries because, if it were, it would be unlike the modern minds of all the other periods of history.

We actually lack the means of unifying our knowledge, of bringing all of the pertinent facts to bear on our problems. We must remember that, until facts are organized,

ences gain new insights into the workings of the brain the
several disciplines within the behavioral sciences are trying
to interpret the heavy demands that society makes on the
individual as it slowly shapes and molds the human mind
into a social as well as a biological entity. Man is not only
an organism adjusting to the physical world in which he
lives but he must also adapt himself as a social being and as
a member of many different groups. The social anthropol-
ogist is concerned with man as more than a social animal,
however, for he studies him as a culture-making, culture-
bearing animal. Herein lies man's uniqueness for man
alone has culture,—culture that creates so many stresses and
strains, that forces the human mind into all sorts of strategies in order to cope with or to evade the conflicts inherent
in group living.

What is *culture* without which social scientists are agreed
that man apparently cannot live? The term *culture* was
coined to express a way of thinking, acting, feeling, believing, that human beings inherit as members of groups. Ralph
Linton defines culture as "the configuration of learned behavior and results of behavior whose elements are shared
and transmitted by members of a society." [3] It is a sort of
helpful shorthand [4] to distinguish learned behavior from
the physical characteristics that we inherit. It is the total
way of life unique in each society. [5]

Two years ago I was teaching in a European University
where there were five hundred students registered from all
over the world. The first question that I asked my inter-
preter was, "How many of these students come from the
United States?" He smiled and said, "I'll tell you tomor-

[3] Ralph Linton, *Cultural Background of Personality*, New York: Apple-
ton-Century-Crofts, 1954, p. 32.
[4] Clyde Kluckhohn, *Mirror For Man*, New York: Whittlesey House, 1949.
[5] Ruth Benedict, *Patterns of Culture*. New York: Houghton-Mifflin, 1934.

row." The next morning I expected statistics but he said that he would tell me at lunch. After the main course was served he took me up to a small balcony overlooking the large dining room. We were to have pie for lunch and he had arranged with the waitresses to serve the pie to the students with the point of the pie away from the individual or to the side. As we stood watching, I saw all the students from Africa, Europe, and Asia eat the pie the way it was placed while all those from the United States turned the point toward themselves. I spent the rest of my month there trying to convince that young man that that was the only *correct* way to eat a piece of pie. That is culture.

It is learned, and learned so well, that it soon becomes habit, performed without thinking. Do you take off your hat or your shoes when you enter a house? No one from the United States has to stop to think—he takes off his hat. No one from Japan has to think either—he takes off his shoes. Thus, in one society it is a sign of respect to bare your head, in another to bare your feet. Each society believes that it has the only correct way. Thus, whether we are born in Sumatra or in the United States, we learn the "correct" habits of cleanliness, of fair play, of right and wrong according to the culture in which we are born. They are simply the "do's" and the "don'ts" of a specific society; they are what "everybody says" and "everybody does."

We also grow into our culture. Growing takes time but it also gives time; it gives time to the adults in a society to teach the patterns of belief and behavior to the growing child. The pervasiveness of culture begins with birth and whether the individual is born in a hygienic hospital in the United States, spanked by a doctor or a nurse to bring the spark of life, or whether, as I saw in a mountain village of Mexico, a father dips the newborn baby into a barrel of water to bring the spark of life,—whichever way it is, with this crisis of birth we first meet the patterns of our culture and we can never escape as long as we live.

It was William Graham Sumner, who published his monumental study *Folkways*[6] in 1906, who pointed out that these customs are the most common forms of cultural control. He defined folkways as "habits of the individual and customs of the society that arise from efforts to satisfy needs."[7] *Mores* for him are "the moral mandates . . . unformulated and undefined[8] . . . (that) pervade and control the ways of thinking in all exigencies of life, returning from the world of abstractions to the world of action[9] . . . social ritual in which we participate unconsciously"[10] whose observation and observance is so important to the welfare of the group that their violation cannot be tolerated. Today, in the 1950's, the terms "folkways" and "mores" are almost household words but it was Dr. Sumner's early recognition of the force of public opinion that defines the mores and the specific part played by the individual mind as the strictest agent in enforcing these moral sanctions (until they have become internalized as "conscience") that was one of his great contributions at the beginning of this century. The solid basis upon which the concept of culture rests lies in these sanctioned "norms," "rules," and "habits" which become the ideas, attitudes, and actions of the individual and the moral guideposts of a society. Further, Sumner recognized his principle that cultures exert an "internal strain toward consistency" so that the many component parts are welded into one integrated whole. Thus culture is more

[6] William Graham Sumner, *Folkways,* Boston: Ginn and Company, 1906.
[7] *Ibid.,* p. iv.
[8] *Ibid.,* p. 56. See pp. 1-74.
[9] *Ibid.,* p. 59.
[10] *Ibid.,* p. 62.

than a collection of isolated and unrelated ways of thinking, acting, and believing. Culture includes "an internalized
system of checks and balances which, although constantly
changing, maintains an equilibrium around a core of inner
consistency." [11]

Culture, then, must be understood as an integrated whole
in which the folkways (right ways) and mores (the moral
mandates) become so internalized that mind no longer has
to make a decision each time it is faced with a problem of
social behavior. The institutions of a society, which Sumner says together with "laws are produced out of mores," [12]
are universal: government, economic life, religion, education, creative arts, warfare are found wherever men live together in groups. But there is a central core uniting all of
the institutions of a particular society. We in our society
have emphasized material culture and economic institutions. We give our greatest rewards to technological achieve-
ment. The Australian Bushmen, on the other hand, have
stressed kinship relations and religious belief; and a man
like Emile Durkheim, the great French sociologist, spent
almost a lifetime trying to unravel the secrets of the religious rituals of the Bushmen. In both societies, from birth
onward, each individual learns by imitation, tradition, and
authority to seek success within the mores of his society.

We believe in individualism in the United States. We
believe that each child should learn to stand on his own
feet and, like the Eskimo hunter who must always hunt
alone, we say that the individual must make his own deci-
sions. The real power of the mores, as Sumner shows, lies
in the use that is made of them by the adults in any society.

[11] Ralph Linton, *Cultural Background of Personality.* New York: Apple-
ton-Century-Crofts, 1954, p. 32.
[12] William Graham Sumner, *Folkways,* Boston: Ginn & Company, 1906,
p. 53.

made the comic books, and Helen of Troy the movies as
well as the stage. The Great Books movement has flourished
with a strong contingent of Greek classics. Translations of
Greek plays, Greek histories, Greek philosophers, are com-
ing out in increasing numbers. Greek mythology is being
presented with literary skill to a wider audience; Hephaestus, for example, will soon be a direct acquaintance in his
own right, and not merely because his Latin name, "Vul-
can," happened to be used for a process in repairing tires.
And we are not dealing merely with a sporadic market or
appeal to a somewhat wider few. There is growing institu-
tional embodiment for the cultivation of Greek literature
and philosophy in the Humanities courses that are becoming standard in the lower years of our colleges—part of the
general attempt, well-intentioned though occasionally blun-
dering, to develop a common cultural core or a basic apper-
ceptive mass of acquaintance, of common knowledge and
symbols for every intelligent person in the modern world,
as once upon a time it was the case for the aristocratic few.

Greek materials are also increasingly permeating theoretical discussion in many fields. The standard text in ser-
mons on class war is Thucydides' description of what happened at Corcyra,[1] how each side slaughtered the other in
turn, and how every vice appeared a virtue when exer-
cized for one's own side. Sociological discussions of what
is natural and what is conventional in human behavior
find many a text in Herodotus: for example, the story of
the Egyptian king who tried the experiment of raising a
child without contact with any language in the hope that
he might find Egyptian to be the natural speech of the un-
taught and so establish the primal antiquity of his people;
he did not let his hopes interfere with his "science," how-

[1] *History of the Peloponnesian War*, Bk. III, ch. x.

ever, and when he heard unfamiliar sounds sent his scribes out to locate what he finally decided was the Phrygian word for "bread"! [2] When psychologists want to take issue with Freud's notion of the Oedipus complex, they approach it through an interpretation of the Oedipus story itself.[3] When a contemporary philosopher wishes to distinguish two views of tragedy in human life, where can he find his clue but in the ancient Greeks—in a contrast between Sophocles' tragedies where conflicts cannot be resolved by human effort, so that Oedipus must fall, and Aeschylus' where anguish and rational striving may work their way through to a better moral order.[4]

I do not think that this incipient "Hellenization" of the American mind, the absorption in the classics, will reach the point where Congress, like the House of Commons in a previous century, will rise as one man to finish the quotation in a classic tongue which a speaker was inspired to begin as the light of dawn came streaming into the chamber. But there is a strong resurgence of interest—it is a social phenomenon of no small proportions—and we may very well ask what is its general tone, what its quality, what its meaning.

One thing it clearly is not, and that is a simple return to the past. I do not deny that there are some for whom it represents a retreat to past glories of the human spirit, as against the deplored "crass materialism" of the modern world. There are some who would make of Plato a new cult, for the aristocrats of the mind; and others who would tie Aristotle in a bundle with Aquinas as an unerring

---

[2] *The History of Herodotus*, II, 2.

[3] See, for example, Patrick Mullahy, *Oedipus: Myth and Complex*, Hermitage Press, 1948.

[4] Philip Blair Rice, *On the Knowledge of Good and Evil* (New York: Random House, 1955), ch. xvi.

guide to contemporary problems. As against these tendencies I would like to make two suggestions. The first is that the Greek materials are too rich, too many-sided, too provocative of the inquiring spirit to allow of a one-sided monopoly. The second is the hypothesis that there is a deep need operative in the contemporary American utilization of ancient Greece, and that is the need for *ideas* in all phases of our life.

Look what happens when a seizure or appropriation is attempted by those who would look backwards. Russell Kirk, for example, hastily building a new conservatism from miscellaneous sources, uses the Greeks to club John Dewey and liberalism: "the terrible events of our time have buried John Dewey and his generation deeper than any Pharaoh. The most old-fashioned and archaic persons in our nation today are those who still try to believe in the inevitability of Progress and the competence of Reason to make men into gods. There are gods among us, true enough: but they are the gods of the copybook headings, returned with fire and sword to remind us how wise were the old Greeks with their talk of hubris and nemesis and catastrophe." [5] Now there was clearly a strong sense of fate and chance and the irrational at different times in Greek life; and this is attractive to the irrationalists today.[6] But this is only a part of the Greek tradition. It also includes the story of Prometheus, who stole the fire from the heavens for the preservation of mankind, and it includes the growth of mathematics and the origin of sci-

---

[5] Russel Kirk, *A Program for Conservatives* (1954), p. 10.

[6] For a scholarly treatment of this aspect of Greek thought, see E. R. Dodds, *The Greeks and the Irrational* (Berkeley and Los Angeles: University of California Press, 1951). He points out, quoting Malraux, that "Western civilization has begun to doubt its own credentials" (p. 254)—a suggestive ground for the increasing attractiveness of irrationalism today.

ence. Many thinkers—for example, Morris Raphael Cohen, in his *The Faith of a Liberal*—trace the western development of the liberal spirit to the Greek beginnings of logic and the scientific outlook.

The Greek image in American thought is preeminently one of rationality. I think of Robinson Jeffers' translation of the speech in Euripides' *Medea* when Jason defends himself against his foresaken wife's bitter denunciation. He says:

> "Some little things that I on my side have done for you
> Ought to be in the books too: as, for example, that I carried you
> Out of the dirt and superstition of Asiatic Cholcis into the rational
> Sunlight of Greece, and the marble music of the Greek temples: is that no benefit?"

"The rational sunlight of Greece" is so fittingly Apollonian. It sums up a great deal—too much to be unwound at this point. And it has all the ambiguity of the situation; for Jason has betrayed Medea and his reasons are smug and blatant rationalization. But this is the modern image; the Greek text has nothing in it about the rational sunlight of Greece. It is even more bitterly ironical, for Jason tells Medea that he brought her out of a barbarian land to Greece where she would know justice and learn to live by law! But then Euripides has sometimes been compared to George Bernard Shaw, and the Athenians of his own day did not take to him too warmly.

Socrates particularly, as an American culture-hero, is the apostle of rational inquiry. Reinhold Niebuhr, who certainly recognizes the irrational elements in man's nature, wrote an article for the Christmas issue of the *Saturday Review of Literature* some years ago on "Christ versus Socrates" in which Socrates figures as the partisan of the reliance on reason, not faith. How far our image is true to the original Socrates is a question of critical scholarship which is not likely to be easily resolved. Albert W. Levi has written a fascinating article [7] in which he traces the enormous variety in the interpretation of Socrates among the philosophers themselves. I quote from his summary: "For John Stuart Mill he is the hero of the civil liberties and the authentic voice of science. For Nietzsche he is the demon of rationalism and the destroyer of art and instinct. For Hegel he is the tragic individualist and the eternal enemy of the political universal. For Kierkegaard he is the existential hero and the sceptical intelligence saved through his actual commitment. These are four ways of interpreting the life and meaning of Socrates. But in a deeper sense they are also four ways of philosophizing in the nineteenth century. It is Socrates' eternal glory that each philosopher must speak of him, but when he does so, he tells us less perhaps of Socrates than of himself." [8]

So much for the inability of any one view to establish a monopoly on the Greek materials. But what of the deeper needs on which the growth of the Greek image rests, the urgent need in all phases of our life today for *ideas?* It may be that we do not welcome them or even are suspicious of them. Dr. Robert M. Hutchins argued in a commencement speech recently that thinking is unpopular in the United States, because it leads to criticism and controversy. He cited a remark made to a friend of his by a great Detroit

[7] Albert W. Levi, "The Idea of Socrates: The Philosophic Hero in the Nineteenth Century," *Journal of the History of Ideas,* xvii, No. 1 (Jan. 1956) pp. 89-108.

[8] *Ibid.,* p. 108.

industrialist: "You are either a Communist or a thinker." [9]
But our distrust and fear may themselves be good evidence
of profound need. Old patterns have worn out, many old
solutions have become threadbare. The world has changed,
and new knowledge has taxed old frameworks of thought
to the limit. This is commonly recognized in all fields of
theoretical endeavor; and in spite of what Dr. Hutchins
has described, it is often recognized by business in its own
field of operation. I recall, for example, a few years ago,
giving a lecture on this campus at the Institute for Humanistic Study for Executives. Here you had a year's liberal arts teaching set up for the Bell Telephone Company,
for the education of promising executives. The explana-
tory materials furnished to me before the lecture were
extremely interesting in their implications. Junior executives, said the memorandum, have to *solve* problems; this
they can learn on the job. But senior executives have to
discover problems; this cannot be learned by rule, it requires insight and broad liberal education! I think that
the same lesson is emerging from all the discussion today
about "thinking-machines" and how much they will be
able to accomplish mechanically. The machine will be
able to make computations and work out logical implications more quickly that men would have had to work on
endlessly in the past. But men will still have to set them
up and analyze the results. The machines may answer the
questions, but men will have to ask them. What is true of
industry and business is even more true of government
and international relations, and that whole web of problems on the solution of which our future so directly depends. And it is still more true of that sensitive probing
into the aims of life which the Book of Ecclesiastes—if I

[9] *New York Times,* June 14, 1957, p. 23.

may interpose the Hebraic in the midst of the Hellenic—expresses as the attempt to "see what it was good for the sons of men that they should do under the heaven all the days of their life." Let me put it succinctly, if somewhat crudely. There is a growing market for ideas in the modern world. The Greeks had ideas—lots of them. Therefore Greek stocks are going up.

In developing this major thesis, I should like to deal first with the impact of the Greek philosophers on the contemporary philosophical outlook in general, and then in greater detail with ethical and social issues. What has been the impact of Greek philosophical materials on American philosophical development in our century? It is difficult to epitomize so vast and varying a theme. To understand why twentieth century philosophers turned with renewed interest to Aristotle and Plato, and even to the pre-Socratics, we have to understand the state which western philosophy had in general reached by the twentieth century in its view of man and his place in the cosmos. A great part of modern philosophy, since the break-up of the mediaeval outlook, can be read as a great schism which appeared in thought and culture and behavior. It was a schism in thought which saw the physical world operating on one set of principles and the human world of knowledge and value entirely set off from it. It was a schism in culture which departmentalized the scientific and humanistic sides of man, leaving him—in Santayana's metaphor—with a science that dealt with the skeleton of things and so frightened poets, and—in Dewey's favorite declamation—with a value domain in which a premium was put on the absence of intelligence. It was a schism in behavior because it made the end and goal of a great part of human activity the exploitation of the material world and indeed the exploitation of one another, and it put the humane spirit and the religious spirit in a separate corner for Sunday or for retirement or perhaps for the after-life.

This great schism was born in the sixteenth and seventeenth centuries as man, having turned from the pursuit of an other-worldly salvation, went on to a conquest of this planet. Its sentiments ranged from the attraction of nature, the love of understanding, and the desire for "the good things of life" to the heat of conquest and the greed of plunder. Its intellectual expression was the philosophy of Descartes with a world that gradually became viewed as a great machine, and a mind that became more and more withdrawn, cut off and alone. Our disrespect for the landscape, the loneliness of the individual in the great metropolis, the anguished dread of the soul of which the contemporary existentialists are constantly painting impressionistic portraits, our vast achievements in the knowledge and control of the physical world coupled with our hesitation to look into ourselves with frankness, and the limitation of our dreams to two cars in every garage (one a suburban, one a Volkswagon)—these are somehow all of a piece. They are not figments of a philosophical imagination, but products of a social and cultural development over several centuries.

The great schism proved inadequate as an intellectual model. It was folly to think that science would stop short at the physical world, and that the development of an evolutionary outlook would leave man's traditional institutions and values untouched. It proved inadequate in the cultural domain because men could not help sensing—as great scientists now often tell us—that science itself is one of the greatest human endeavors, and because a value field without intellectual controls yields not spirituality but worldliness or blind wilfulness and the quest for irresponsible power, or sometimes an unthinking conservatism or an irresponsible mysticism. It proved inadequate in behavior because, in the trite phrase, the predatory pursuit of means without concern for the basic ends of man institutionalized chaos in social and political life.

The Greek image in twentieth century philosophy offers the vision of a unified order of nature which overcomes the schisms and dissatisfying fragmentation of the later-day philosophies. And it offers it in a form which predates the mediaeval supernaturalist unity—the world of Dante—to which for the modern there can be no return. Of course there may be a component of the desire to return to childhood in the wistful pursuit of the Greek vision in our time, a search for a lost hope and an irrecoverable innocence. But I do not think this is its essence. For it is less a search for the answers that the Greek philosophers gave than for inspiration about questions and ideas and spirit of inquiry. This is seen, for one thing, in the fact that all philosophical points of view are equally attracted.

Philosophical materialists in their concern with material substance and change and the construction of a unified evolutionary outlook on man and the cosmos are fascinated by the confident sweep of the early pre-Socratics who ask whether everything is made of the same water or fire or indeterminate stuff, and try to explain the whole order of nature and man on the basis of familiar processes. The fragments of the pre-Socratics are being increasingly scrutinized today. And since the missing pieces predominate in this picture-puzzle, you can make of it anything you will, and you will find the first ancestors of any philosophy you hold to. But the general attempt is clear, and it is precisely this quest for unified explanation that compellingly attracts today.

The philosophical idealists are all drawn to Plato. Plato is the father of philosophical idealism, with its emphasis on the eternal and the interpretation of reality in terms of spirit. Whitehead says somewhere that all western philosophy is a footnote to Plato. But why should the ancestral form be so attractive to idealists today, when they have the grandiose historical Hegelian idealism or the Schopenhauerian voluntarism, or a whole set of other nineteenth century varieties to choose from? Perhaps Whitehead's own career is the best explanation. Whitehead made profound contributions in mathematical logic and was thoroughly grounded in modern science, and then went to the history of philosophy in search of a synthesis to override the schisms of the past three hundred years. Plato, too, we must recall, had found his inspiration in mathematics and logic. What appeals in our time is not then the mystical strain, not even the rejection of the material changing world as a shadowy image of the eternal real. It is rather his rational dialectic and the unified quest of the spirit for an intellectual world-formula. And it is perhaps also his fusion of this quest with the guidance of life, the searching penetration of the ideal in every corner of existence. And so even a Santayana, whose own metaphysics is a kind of biological-chemical materialism, can make a serious attempt to naturalize the Platonic ideal and to see all human life as the light of the ideal generated from the friction of material forces.

The naturalistically minded philosophers, however, predominantly gravitate to Aristotle. They try to achieve a unified view of man and the cosmos by accepting, extend-

ing and systematizing the scientific way of looking at the
world, with its powerful base in the physical sciences and
its growing insight into the processes of biological evolution and human development. And in Aristotle, once one
gets beyond the fixed and static order that so attracted the
mediaevals, there is a confident assurance that it is one
world. This is not just a slogan; he works it out in the de-
tails of his fundamental conceptions. To Aristotle it seems
the most natural thing in the world that underlying quali-
tative changes there should be spatial changes of the matter involved, or that the soul should be related to the body
as cutting is to the axe or seeing to the eye. In Aristotle
you find the picture of a rising order of nature in which
therefore man's thinking is as proper an exercise of his
capacities as a stone's fall is of the stone's capacities. The
unity in the whole outlook is not merely metaphysical, it
is also cultural. There is no sharp break between ethics
and politics on the one side or ethics and psychology on
the other. Man's good emerges from his nature, which is
rooted in his biology and psychology and has its expression in social relations. Morality is thus in large part practice and education, not merely a name for inner reactions
of the spirit. Nor again are the humanities set off from
the knowledge of nature and man, whether it be the question of tragedy or the training of the lawyer and the rheto-
rician.

To restore a unified view of man and the universe in
such an Aristotelian spirit does not mean a dehumaniza-
tion of man, any more than it need mean a teleological-
religious view of the motion of the heavenly bodies. But
it does mean that our conception of science and its results
is also broadened. As Woodbridge used to put it—and
Woodbridge (the source of inspiration for the contem-

porary Columbia naturalistic philosophers) was very self-conscious about what he sought in Aristotle—to study the nature of man is also to learn about the nature of nature.[10] Atoms should not be regarded as merely entities capable of certain types of motion—or as we are now likely to conjure up the image, of explosion. Since you and I are made of atoms, and we are now discussing philosophy, it follows that atoms can discuss philosophy, when they properly congregate about the business, in the due and proper organization of self-conscious human beings! And this does not mean, as Lucretius warns us in his *De Rerum Natura,* that we should expect atoms to shake their sides with laughter just because we are laughing. There is a calculated naïveté about such philosophizing that constitutes it almost a methodological principle. It says something profound much more simply than we could by invoking some "principle of emergence" or "the whole is greater than the sum of its parts" or the like. This is another virtue of the ancient materials. You see philosophical ideas crystallizing. Instead of talking about the *essence* of something you find Aristotle saying "the what-it-is." Instead of "final cause" you find "the for-the-sake-of-what." And so on.

Let me take the more detailed example from ethics and social philosophy, and show in a more specific way the impact of the Greek materials on our ideas. Suppose we take the Greek idea of democracy. Of course we know that the intellectual influence of Greek political thought and experience on American thought is not a new phenomenon. It is common knowledge that the fathers of the constitution were subject to this influence. I take my edition of *The Federalist* from my shelves; it has no index, and so I

[10] F. J. E. Woodbridge, "The Nature of Man," in his *Nature and Mind,* New York, Columbia University Press, 1937.

open it at random. The very first page to come before my eyes refers to the Achaean League, an ancient Greek federalist experiment (XLIV). I leaf a few pages and light on the argument: "In all very numerous assemblies, of whatever characters composed, passion never fails to wrest the sceptre from reason. Had every Athenian citizen been a Socrates, every Athenian assembly would still have been a mob" (LIV). A glance here and there turns up a reference to Sparta and another to Pericles; let this suffice as my homage to the statistical-experimental method. Professor Borghese has shown that Pericles' famous funeral oration in which the nature of the Athenian democratic idea is expounded, was freshly in Lincoln's mind when he wrote the Gettysburg address.[11] But we are not now concerned with the limited role of Greek political ideas when classical education loomed large but education itself was limited. What of the contemporary scene?

Pericles' funeral speech still remains one of the basic expressions of the democratic spirit, with its emphasis on the wide participation of citizens in public life, the critical role of discussion in determining, not thwarting, action, its faith in the common man, its insistence on liberty in individual life not merely against coercion but against others looking askance, and so on. I pass over its obvious limitations in accepting the exclusion of women from public life, as well as in ignoring the slave basis of its own society. But modern political realism has developed the habit of looking beyond ideals and programs to operative procedures. And so, in evaluating Athenian democracy we look on in Thucydides to other parts—the imperialistic policy of Athens and its wanton attack on Melos, with the overt contention that justice is a question only between

[11] "Pericles and Lincoln," *Common Cause*, 1948, vol. iii.

equals in power, the demagogic Cleon's warning to the Athenians that their empire rests on force and that without stern punishment of rebellion they will lose their hold,[12] and so on. This leads us directly to the question what the ancients themselves thought of democracy when they came to reflect about it philosophically.

Our best sources here, of course, are Plato's *Republic* and Aristotle's *Politics*. Let us look at the impact of Plato's dialogue in contemporary thought, and supplement it with reference to Aristotle's ideas. The *Republic* is the widest read today of Plato's works—used as one of the "great books," as a classic in studying political theory, education, philosophy, and so on. Now Plato here is clearly antagonistic to democracy, although in a later work he concluded that while it can do the least good, it can also do the least harm. What, as an American reader who is generally a believer in democracy, do you find yourself feeling about Plato's discussion? Are you shaken by the full scope of the authoritarian utopia he presents? Recall his arguments. He appeals to a principle of justice, that every man do that for which he is best fit. He applies this division of labor idea to taking care of society, that is, protecting it against outside attack in the wars that he regards as inevitable, and against internal subversion. Thus he generates a three-class state in which the wisest determine fundamental policy, the courageous administrators carry it out, and the mass of the people temperately follow it. He gives you a picture of controlled education in which their role and virtues are stamped upon each group, and especially the intellect awakened and sharpened in the guardian classes. He

[12] Thucydides' *History of the Peloponnesian War*, III, ch. ix. Incidentally, Pericles admits as much in another speech: "For what you hold is, to speak somewhat plainly, a tyranny; to take it perhaps was wrong, but to let it go is unsafe." (II, ch. vii.)

probes into the nature of man to justify these class distinctions, and finds—to use his own metaphor—that each of us is three in one: a man (reason), a lion (will, spirit, or ambitious energy), a dragon (the many-headed hydra of desire, capriciously seeking release from tension without looking ahead or to the whole of life, a veritable Freudian Id). He fashions an élite out of the upper two groups, with detailed arrangements of a separate communal life to ensure unyielding devotion to the task of governing for the common welfare. He justifies the rule of his top élite by invoking a metaphysics of an eternal universal reality which only the awakened intellect can attempt to grasp, and by comparison with which all of the changing world of particular things is an appearance, a shadow on the screen in the prison cave of life—a kind of three-dimensional movie. And when all this is done, you see him tracing the decline and fall of the ideal state, passage through a Spartan-type or, if you like, feudal-type society to the emergence of an oligarchic rule of the rich, with the monetary spirit permeating values in all fields, and then from it— second from the bottom—there emerges democracy. And now Plato launches an attack on its sacred slogans. Liberty is simply the demand for rampant individual acquisitive caprice. Equality is the demand for similar treatment for unequals. Everybody rules and becomes a law to himself. Our common retort, "Well, I'm entitled to my opinion" would have seemed, for Plato, like making a species of private property, with a sign "No trespassing" out of shadows of the image of truth. And democracy, says Plato, by opening the door so wide for the dragon in each of us, corrupts the best among us, brings the struggle of rich and poor to white heat, and is ever on the verge of succumbing to gangster control guided by unprincipled power-seeking motives. There is the challenge, woven with superb dialectic. What will you do with it?

Some may shunt it aside, saying, "Of course, he's right. But it's not us he's talking about. We have a representative democracy, not a direct democracy." But does this face the issues? Have we gained much if Plato would classify us as a moderate oligarchy instead?

You may be won over by the vision of the Platonic philosopher with his eyes fixed on the Idea of the Good. Then you may say, "He's right, but it's a dream. Too bad we don't have such guardians. Meanwhile we have to get along as best as we can by finding the best rulers available and letting the people keep some control over them, just to check against corruption." Aristotle in many respects talks like a sceptical Platonist. He wants a government of laws, not men, because although he recognizes that it is better to be cured by the doctor than by the text-book, he just can't be sure that the doctor may not be leagued with his enemies to destroy him! And he is very realistic—if you get a single man way above the rest, why then have monarchy. If many are equally good, then why shouldn't they all take part in ruling? It all depends. Anyhow, says Aristotle, the real issues of his day are the battle of oligarchy and democracy—not treated abstractly, but in terms of the battle of the rich and the poor. You want a middle type of government which will avoid the desperation of the poverty-stricken and the arrogance of the wealthy. Compromise is a matter of detailed mediation.

In American democracy there have been many tendencies along these lines—a kind of Platonism within the democratic framework. Its essence is the equation of the people with the great beast, whether Hamilton said it or not. Central emphasis falls then on the need for a veto, a restrictive power over the masses, the rule of the lower self by the higher self. You find it in a writer like Irving Babbitt who says: "If we analyze realistically the popular will, we find that it means the will of a multitude of men who are more and more emancipated from traditional standards and more and more given over to what I have termed the irresponsible quest of thrills." [13] Babbitt contrasts the Washingtonian liberal who is less expansive in his attitude to the natural man, with the Jeffersonian liberal who has faith in the goodness of the natural man. Nowadays the contrast has shifted from two types of liberalism to liberalism versus the new conservatism, and the latter has tried to build up John Adams to counterbalance Thomas Jefferson. Sometimes in American political thought we have even found the claim that America is not properly to be regarded as a democracy; it was only intended to be a republic! The people, in short, may pass on how their rulers have served in office, and select fresh rulers, but they must not take a hand in rule themselves.

Another reaction to Plato's *Republic* is to accept its argument, but attenuate it. "After all," you may say, "Plato is not really concerned with a specific form. He is giving us philosophical principles. No matter how rulers come to their position, don't you find three types of people —the wise deliberative type, the executive type, and the rest of us concerned with their own narrow interests? It isn't a question of turning America into a Platonic mold, but of recognizing the basic principles, and doing more consciously what we are now doing in a mixed sort of way."

Others, however, will not allow acceptance on any terms. The battle against Plato has been very intense. Karl R.

[13] Irving Babbitt, *Democracy and Leadership,* New York: Houghton Mifflin, 1924, p. 267.

Popper, for example, in his well-known *The Open Society and Its Enemies,* launches a full-scale attack from the point of view of a free enterprise philosophy; Plato is marked as enemy number one, the fountainhead of totalitarianism. Alban D. Winspear, in *The Genesis of Plato's Thought,* propounds a Marxian view of Plato as the ideological defender of a declining class. If you wish to read an analysis of Plato by a leading British socialist, see R. H. S. Crossman's *Plato Today*. Crossman has Plato also give his comments on modern life. And there have been many others. Criticisms have been wide and varied enough to prompt Ronald B. Levinson to write a book entitled *In Defense of Plato*. It is not exaggeration to say that the battle over Plato is a serious area in contemporary social philosophy.

Now suppose you take none of these paths, but instead are put on your mettle and want to defend liberty and equality and the democratic idea. Suppose that in a Jeffersonian spirit you feel that even if Plato's ideal state were wholly and successfully achieved as he maps it, it would still be undesirable because it would be exercising paternal dominion over the mass of men and they would be followers rather than individuals exercising thought and initiative. How would you go about the defense? Look at what Plato has made you do. You would have to start from the beginning and analyze each of his fundamental ideas. I can only indicate by suggestion what sort of a job lies ahead of you. You will have to challenge his fundamental interpretation of justice—for example you may argue that each man doing what he is best fit for does not mean division of men into classes, that the kind of division of labor a democracy envisages may be a division of jobs but not a placing or stereotyping and freezing of men; or that modern conditions make the mobility of interest a real possi-

bility. You will have to challenge his initial assumption
that war is inevitable because of the passions and desires
of men. In fact you can find in Plato himself the assumption that scarcity underlies war,[14] and you may wonder
whether he isn't taking this scarcity too much for granted,
perhaps because of its unavoidable presence in the ancient
world. But if this is so, then maybe large parts of his social
philosophy reflect the fundamental fact of scarcity rather
than the assumed acquisitive nature of the dragon. Aristotle helps you out here, for he points out in an aside,
even though he defends slavery, that if you had automa-
tion things would be different: "If every instrument could
accomplish its own work, obeying or anticipating the will
of others, like the statues of Daedalus or the tripods of
Hephaestus, which, says the poet (Homer, *Iliad,* xviii, 376),
'of their own accord entered the assembly of the Gods';
if, in like manner, the shuttle would weave and the plec-
trum touch the lyre without a hand to guide them, chief
workmen would not want servants, nor masters slaves." [15]
And now you are left with the haunting suspicion that a
great deal of traditional ethical and social theory may stem
from conditions of the world of the past which may be today undergoing profound change. There is no shortcut
then to your inquiry.

And so you proceed. Is Plato's theory of the nature of
man correct? Or is it a view tailor-made to support the
kind of regimented society he builds on it? Of course if
most men are at bottom dragons, then constant repression
is required. But may not the dragonish quality itself re-

[14] In *Republic* II, pp. 373-374, when it is decided to admit some luxuries
into the community. This, says Socrates, means war because there isn't
enough land to support luxuries; you will need a slice of your neighbors'
land and they will need a slice of yours.
[15] *Politics,* 1253 b 34 ff.

flect the cultural influence of a regimented society or of a chaotic society? May not human nature be more neutral, like the block of marble out of which the artist fashions his work? (The metaphor is Aristotle's.) And so you have to explore history and social psychology to establish whether you are correct or Plato is—for your view also may be tailor-made for your democratic conceptions. And then you move on to education, and truth and reality. What are the character effects of a controlled education? Or what the differential effects of different patterns of control? Can any guardians claim infallibility, as Plato's almost seem to do? Does the fact that no man is infallible require instead—in the interests of finding truth—the kind of liberal free structure that John Stuart Mill envisaged in his *Liberty* rather than the Platonic regulation by the wise? Is Plato's picture of reality too dependent on a special interpretation of mathematics? If so, what is the effect of modern changes in the conception of mathematics? Is the possibility of non-Euclidean geometries and the changed treatment of axioms to which it gave rise—as relational structures rather than ultimate truths, or imaginative possibilities rather than necessary actualities—a real foundation stone, as some have claimed, for the liberal temper with its constant sense of alternatives, and the democratic social framework?

Do you think that is enough? No, there is still the philosophy of history that interprets the unstable character of democracy, and the tendency to develp despotism, as the inherent character of democracy itself. Can you work out an opposing theory to show that despotism is a consequence of, say, special conditions of economic life and class conflict, or the like, so that the cure for the instability

cal presuppositions, they imposed on the American imagination those of New England. I have been told that even in the South well-educated young ladies used to think it vulgar to admire Spanish moss because it doesn't appear in the lyrics of Mr. Longfellow. That may be an exaggeration, but I know for myself that though I lived in Illinois, and saw the summer and winter there for myself, still whenever I thought of treating such phenomena poetically, I thought in terms of the imagery imparted by my grammar-school teacher's readings from the New England poets. We all saw the prairie seasons through Yankee eyes, until suddenly the Middle West found its own voice; Edgar Lee Masters, Vachel Lindsay, Carl Sandburg made Spoon River, Springfield, and the hog-butcher to the world as honorable themes for poetry as the churchyard at Cambridge. A great part of the supposedly revolutionary impact of those Chicago writers in the 1920's was simply that they did mention what was around them. Because that much now seems obvious—we do not expect a poet in Carmel to use the backdrop of Haverhill, Massachusetts— it is difficult to appreciate the violence of the jolt they administered to the dominant orthodoxy. Hence it may seem that those once insurgent geniuses have worn a little thin; we even find in contemporary criticism certain slight, judicious, efforts to rehabilitate the once spreading reputation of Henry Wadsworth Longfellow.

Of course, this uprising against domination by the New England Household Poets (Bryant, even though he lived most of his life in New York was counted one of them, because his nature scenes were the Berkshires) was part of a multifold rejection in American culture around 1920 of the hegemony of New England. This strain in the revolt of that irreverent decade—a period often nowadays as falsely glamorized as to us in the actual 1920's was the "mauve decade" of the '90's—is too large a subject to be more than mentioned here, but the fact that such a protest was made, and made emphatically, is a major reason why today there should be any interest at all in my topic. In the ubiquitous denunciations of the "Puritan" which enlivened that joyous—well, not too joyous—time, and which still echo in occasional growls, the real target was never the historical Puritan of the seventeenth century— about him the young rebels knew little and cared less— but the image of culture, of control of emotion, monogamy, temperance (or worse), which nineteenth-century New England had supposedly foisted on the country. Years ago George Santayana gave it a more accurate name, "The Genteel Tradition," yet he also, as in his tract disguised as a novel, *The Last Puritan,* argued that the sterile genteelism of New England was a Puritanism gone to seed. So, voices arose all over the land—from the south-side of Chicago; from St. Paul, Minnesota; from Charleston, South Carolina; from the Barbary Coast of San Francisco; from Greenwich Village; and then for a while a whole chorus from the Left Bank of Paris—all proclaiming the independence of the American mind from Puritanism and from prohibition. What was meant in effect was that the other regions were throwing off the yoke of New England. Indeed, hundreds of young New Englanders enthusiastically joined the wrecking crews.

All this, as I say, had nothing really to do with the Puritan heritage which the New England colonists had built into the foundations of the nation. Through successive modifications, divisions, transformations, Puritan theology has had a continuous history in America, and this never entered seriously into any of 1920's revolts against New

England. If in the cold-water flats around Washington Square among bands of fugitives from Gopher Prairie, meeting over a bath-tub full of gin to tell each other the inner mystery of this strange new apparition (smuggled through the customs) called *Ulysses*, the rebellion was sometimes proclaimed against Protestant doctrine as well as against the school marm's Mr. Longfellow, that aspect of their discourse was purely rhetorical and is of little worth to the historian. After all, the Neo-Orthodoxy, so-called, of Rheinhold and Richard Niebuhr is as much a product of the 1920's as the novels of F. Scott Fitzgerald. We can see that continuity in the development of American religious experience was not rudely broken by the emotional upheavals of post-World War I, though it was, in more fundamental ways, affected. But in the realms of literary taste and in the popular conception of artistic purpose, a real and permanent revolution was indeed enacted. The simplest way to describe it, or to designate what it did, is to say that it dethroned the cultural supremacy of New England.

I for one believe that it was high time this "sans-culottism" appeared. Possibly some of you know the book published in 1900 by my distinguished predecessor at Harvard, Barrett Wendell, *A Literary History of America*. It is a pioneer work, and does not always merit the contempt which now is automatically poured upon it. Still, the amusing fact about it is undeniable: after a cursory survey of the colonial and revolutionary periods (giving special attention and space to Cotton Mather), and brief glances at Irving, Cooper and Poe, the substance of the book is two long portions called "The Renaissance of New England," after which comes a very brief section, almost an appendix, arrogantly entitled "The Rest of the Story." It has a fifteen-page piece on Whitman, which is mainly a demonstration that Whitman's notion of absolute equality is altogether foreign to the facts of American life and thought (as had been evidenced, according to Wendell, throughout the literature of New England, wherein not even Emerson entirely succumbed to the absurdity), but which is chiefly known to derisive fame because it characterizes "Crossing Brooklyn Ferry" as confused, inarticulate, and "surging in a mad kind of rhythm which sounds as if hexameters were trying to bubble through sewage."

Barrett Wendell was entirely a product of that late nineteenth-century culture of New England against which the attacks of the 1920's were levelled. After the battle was over and the insurgents had won their victory, Mr. Van Wyck Brooks endeavored to be gracious to this era by calling his book about it *New England: Indian Summer*. Probably many people read it—as a great many at least purchased it—because they really have a nostalgia for the serenity, the security, the courtesy which that age seemed to offer—certainly these it appeared to offer in ample measure as Mr. Brooks presented it. But actually that New England is an imaginary home to which none of us can go back any more—even supposing for a moment, what I am sure is untrue, that it ever was such an idyllic paradise. While critics, or such bludgeoners as H. L. Mencken, were demolishing its pretensions, a new historian of American thought and letters emerged in 1926. He came from the West, from the state of Washington; after Vernon Louis Parrington's *Main Currents in American Thought* nobody—not even the most inbred Harvard-Bostonian scholar—could ever dare again to survey the scene from the point of view of a Barrett Wendell.

I suppose that almost every chapter Parrington wrote

has been superseded by the rush of later research; the truth seems to be that even then he worked out of very limited sources. Still, the book, even though tragically uncompleted, is a monument of scholarship in the whole field of what we now call "American Civilization" or, less boastfully, "American Studies." Anyone alive in 1926 who was responding to the fresh interest in things American which blew like a gale across the country will remember the excitement of Parrington. There were a hundred illuminations in it—the seemingly comprehensive sweep of the South and the West, for instance—but one of the more vibrant was his resolute cutting down to size of Harvard University and the orthodox New England poets. He did not orate, he was no barbarian from without the walls, but in quiet, measured tones he ticked off the mentality of Back Bay:

> The immediate consequence of this concern for defensive breastwork was the reign of the genteel in life and letters, a reign that set up a court of critical jurisdiction over the domain of American letters. The essence of the genteel was a refined ethicism, that professed to discover the highest virtue in shutting one's eyes to disagreeable fact, and the highest law in the law of convention. . . . The first of literary commandments was the commandment of reticence.

In the general joy that this at last was publicly said, and said in such a way that it could never be forgotten, many neglected to notice that Barrett Wendell had just barely managed to end his chapter of Whitman with a quotation (I think from his colleague Charles Eliot Norton) to the effect that a man who could idealize the East River "is the only one who points out the stuff of which perhaps the new American literature of the future may in time be made." But then, though this is said, it is weakly said; so Barrett Wendell gets no great credit for it, any more than he gets credit for having mentioned Melville, on page 229, because it is obvious he had never read Melville, knew of him only from Robert Louis Stevenson's admiration for Melville's South Sea travels, and managed to spell Melville's first name with two "n's"!

Remaining a moment longer with the contrast of Wendell and Parrington—if I may do so without becoming tedious, for I know no better way of getting some historical perspectives on our problem—it is worth noting that Parrington entertained no hostility to New England as such. On the contrary, he adored its militant reforming zeal, its Puritan conscience when enlisted on the side of social justice instead of when sublimated into genteel reticence. His heroes out of nineteenth-century New England were William Lloyd Garrison, John G. Whittier, Harriet Beecher Stowe, Theodore Parker, Edmund Quincy, Wendell Phillips. The head and front of the Brahmins' offence, as Parrington saw it, was that they "took it ill when those barriers were assaulted by rude militants, and when indisputable Brahmins—men like Edmund Quincy and Wendell Phillips—took part in the assault, the Back Bay regarded them as more than a little queer."

Here the contrast with Barrett Wendell could not possibly be more extreme. Wendell had to write a chapter on "The Antislavery Movement," which he did with obvious loathing. In palliation of Theodore Parker's extremely bad manners, Wendell wrote, "there might be pleaded the excuse that [he], like Garrison, sprang from the lower class of New England which never intimately understood its social superiors." The self-made man, he moralized, can rarely quite outgrow all the limitations of his origin—thus paraphrasing Dr. Holmes's eminently Bostonian quip that the self-made man is necessarily an ill-made one. But, Wendell continued, his enmity becoming a screech, "No such excuse may be pleaded for the two other antislavery orators who are best remembered—Wendell Phillips and Charles Sumner." For Wendell Phillips, Barrett Wendell's only comment was that at the end of his life he did nothing but "exhibit the somewhat senile vagaries of a character whose leading passion seems to have become an ardour for disagreement with mankind." As for the whole movement, though of course slavery was an evil, Barrett Wendell sees in it a Yankee carry-over of a hypocritical trait of the English: "For no peculiarity has been more characteristic of the native English than a passion to reform other people than themselves, trusting meantime that God will help those who forcibly help somebody else."

One of the points Parrington heavily underscored in expressing his admiration for Wendell Phillips was that Phillips did not concentrate all his reforming zeal on abolition, that he did not give over being an agitator after Appomattox, but that he continued to fight for all liberal reforms, even for the rights of labor. For Barrett Wendell, these were senile crotchets. Here then we have two opposite poles from which to evaluate our own thinking, once we attempt to appraise our inheritance from nineteenth-century New England, especially when we meditate upon that ferment of reform which was so cataclysmic a part of its spiritual expression. And we have to take account of the whole tremendous impulse, not just of abolitionism. In education, economics, sexual relations, religion, it was equally disruptive, equally extravagant, equally vociferous, equally noble and absurd.

Whereupon we run smack against an interesting phenomenon: the liberal mentality which came of age and so to free expression in the 1920's—of which Parrington was the perfect representative—took delight at one and the same time in denigrating the Brahmins of New England and in exalting its militant radicals. This seemed in 1926 eminently logical. After all, slavery was an evil, it did have to be abolished, at a terrible cost; did this not make the abolitionists prophets and heroes? And the other reforms —in how many of them had not the New England cranks also proved to be prophets—Horace Mann, Margaret Fuller, the enthusiasts of Brook Farm? Suppose they were sometimes comic in their eagerness, innocent in their dreams of how easy it would be to improve mankind? Have they not all been vindicated? Henry James thought he was treating Elizabeth Peabody with loving though amused consideration when he presented her as "Miss Birdseye" in *The Bostonians* of 1880, but he had to learn even then that in America these warriors of the once ridiculed newnesses had survived into a veneration which could no longer be treated with even a taint of derision.

The result has been that over what I may summarily call the liberal mentality—meaning that which inspired Parrington and which still informs upright citizens of this republic—New England continued to exercise a conceptual hegemony. Only now, it was a moral superiority rather than a literary one. If Longfellow appeared more and more tepid, and Dr. Holmes emerged as a parochial snob, still John Brown was a veritable martyr. There was no reason not to repeat with approval Emerson's statement that Brown "made the gallows glorious as the cross." Yes, by the civil code he had to be hanged, but did not the boys in blue march to bloody victory singing that while his body lay a-mouldering in the grave, his soul went marching on? And John Brown was the very essence of New England's reforming passion.

I need hardly point out that in the climate of today none of these positions seems quite so clear as it did to men of Parrington's generation and persuasion. In this day of the F. B. I., what sort of shrift would a creature get who organizes a plot to overthrow by force and violence anything in the social structure of which he disapproves on ideological grounds? How much tolerance would a reformer receive who calls the Constitution of the United States (as William Lloyd Garrison actually did) "A Covenant with Death and an Agreement with Hell"? And, when the historian comes, critically and detachedly to study the period, he is obliged to ask whether abolitionists actually did have any effect on the ultimate emancipation other than to exacerbate the discussion so that war, protracted war, became inevitable? And then, how many of them, once they took unto themselves the smug credit for having launched the crusade, thereafter basked in the glory, thereafter showed no concern whatsoever for the thickening crowd of evils that came in the wake of the Civil War?

I do not take seriously the literature which recently enjoyed a vogue under the catch-phrase, "The New Conservatism." But it is no doubt a symptom of our times; certainly there is much talk about the "conformism" of our age. Even if that be exaggerated, I think this much is indisputable: the reforming spirit of nineteenth-century New England gloried in chanting that Wrong was always on the throne and Right enchained at its feet; from this persuasion it derived the energy to go forth and do battle for the Lord. This "Hebraic zeal"—as it is sometimes called —transmitted itself from New England to the various protest movements of later decades. Populism and the Progressive Party included many latter-day New Englanders in their leadership; at Chicago in 1912 the rally cry was, "We stand at Armageddon." All this seemed to be entirely in the grand manner of Garrison and Theodore Parker.

Historians of a larger sophistication, with more subtle tools for sociological dissection, are now giving us rather different accounts of these idealistic uprisings. They note, for instance, that nothing much came of them, that they petered out as soon as the protestants got from government a few slices of the augmenting prosperity. The New England style of moral exhortation begins to seem at best an ethical rationalization for highly mundane strategies, at worst a form of propagandistic demagoguery. And so a suspicion has been suggested: was the reformist surge in pure New England of the 1840's entirely so selfless? Even though Back Bay found reformism vulgar, still New England, with its burgeoning factories, did need to strike down the South, to wreck the plantation economy, and to persuade what was left of the country to indulge it with a protective tariff. And as for the other reformers—when you study some of them closely, are they not unlovely egotists of whom Nathaniel Hawthorne gave the prototype in his Hollingsworth of *The Blithedale Romance?*

Just as soon as you raise queries of these sorts—which, as I say, are uncomfortable—you find yourself realizing (as too few students of literature and religion do) that after 1815 New England was gaining an ascendency over the mind of America not only by flooding it with the irresistibly popular verses of its Household Poets or by calling it sternly to task in the name of moral idealism, but less spectacularly though more remorselessly it was leading American society into the Industrial Revolution. This is hardly the place to insert a survey of American economic development. But the rough outlines are familiar. It all begins with the supremely ironic joke of American history: agrarian Mr. Jefferson, believing that the preservation of this rural economy depended on keeping it unentangled with Europe, imposed on the Atlantic ports the Embargo of 1807, and so turned New Englanders from the ocean to the rivers. Then the story jumps ahead, as a result of a Yankee trick: Francis Lowell, visiting England from 1810 to 1812, spent more weeks walking the aisles of cotton factories than of cathedrals, and stored his clever head with plans for the machines of which the British, striving to protect their monopoly, would not tell the secrets. By 1814 his loom was functioning in Waltham, Massachusetts.

One has always to remember that in New England there were other forms of aesthetic indulgence than the sweetly melancholy lyrics of Longfellow. When Francis Lowell exhibited his loom to Nathan Appleton (who had been so sceptical that he would advance Lowell only five of the ten thousand dollars Lowell needed), Appleton saw the portent: "I well recollect the state of admiration and satisfaction with which we sat by the hour, watching the beautiful movement of this new and wonderful machine, destined as it evidently was, to change the character of all textile industry."

It not only changed the character, it introduced acceleration. Any good textbook, of which there are several, will quickly show the imbalance between the mechanical facilities of New England as against the rest of the country combined: in 1860, sixty-nine per cent of the cotton manufacturing was concentrated in the region; at that date it was the center for the manufacture of smaller metal products. With the canals and railroads, the revolution spread rapidly westward across the northern tier of states, but it expanded out of New England.

Historians point out "reasons" for this rapid transformation of New England's economy. The availability of water-power is clearly central, as is the existence of an intelligent populace which could quickly master skilled manual operations. As the hard soil was becoming harder, hundreds who would not go to Ohio went to Lowell and Pawtucket. Yet I am strongly of the feeling that the amazing extent and speed of the process can not wholly be explained by purely economic factors. It is not enough to account for these by phrases like "Yankee ingenuity," "the land of steady habits," or a high concentration of what Max Weber taught us to call "the Protestant ethic." Finally, abandoning historical causality altogether, you permit yourself the purely intuitive divination that here, at the beginning of the dramatic century was a culture with a highly developed personality, amazingly homogeneous despite its many divisions and its inner animosities. We may then hazard a guess that we get some sense of what was really the configuration of this culture when we see that it was, at one and the same time, expressed in the genteel elegance of the Brahmins, in the fiery energies of the reformers, and in Nathan Appleton's ecstatic encounter with beauty in a power loom.

There is always the danger, in trying to describe a complex business in a short time, of over-simplification; I assure you that the pattern of nineteenth-century New England is a bit more incoherent than I am making it seem. Still, to repeat, at the beginning of the century, it was remarkably homogeneous. And if these three elements seem at first sight to have little in common, on second thought, we can see that they join hands to form, so to speak, three sides of a quadrilateral. The mind of Brahmin gentility is obviously related on one side to the success of the Industrial Revolution. James Russell Lowell was, after all, a Lowell, and Longfellow married Nathan Appleton's daughter, and Nathan bought Craigie House on Brattle Street as a wedding present for them. Dr. Holmes, in his peculiar manner, says some of the most brutally realistic things about the value of money, the importance of a social position backed by wealth, that cynicism could achieve. Yet on the other side, while Brahmin gentility disliked the uproar of reform, it is allied to that phenomenon by its high ethical devotion. Back Bay would take care not to become abolitionist, but it would never accept the Southern thesis that slavery was ethically justifiable; when the fight had to come, young Brahmins fought gallantly, ferociously, even though it seemed shocking to men like Garrison that they should fight without sharing his conviction. And across from each other, the reforming spirit and the business spirit of New England, which contended on the surface against each other, are united underneath that surface by their derivation from the tremendous earnestness of the Puritan heritage. Whatever they did, they did hard.

If the three may thus be said to link at the corners, at least enough to give us a discussable outline of coherence, we should then need a fourth side to complete my rhetorical design. We have an east, with a northern and southern flank reaching out from it, but have we west? And if such there be, does it join the dance?

Emerson artfully concluded the second *Series* of his *Essays* with one called "New England Reformers." It is probably little read today; I have difficulty explaining to students why, along with such lofty topics as Love, Friendship, Experience, The Poet, Emerson should have been obliged to descend to this hub-bub. But the reason we today are puzzled is that we forget with what importunity the reforming spirit pressed upon the spirit of sensitive, intelligent youth. It threatened to gobble up the mind, it was an invasion of privacy, it had to be resisted. Emerson's essay was truly an appropriate rear-guard for his two series; it stands in the gap, holding off the most dangerous or insidious enemy, while his free thoughts make good their escape, while they can run wild.

When taken in the context of the 1840's, Emerson's inventory of the causes advocated by the New England reformers is one of the few funny passages he ever wrote; he starts off with the more serious issues, then develops his list into slapstick:

> Even the insect world was to be defended,—that had been too long neglected, and a society for the protection of ground-worms, slugs, and mosquitoes was to be incorporated without delay. With these appeared the adepts of homeopathy, of hydropathy, of mesmerism, of phrenology, and their wonderful theories of the Christian miracles. Others assailed particular vocations, as that of the lawyer, that of the merchant, of the manufacturer, of the clergyman, of the scholar. Others attacked the institution of marriage, as the fountain of social evils. Others devoted themselves to the worrying of churches and meetings for public worship; and the fertile forms of antinomianism among the elder puritans seemed to have their match in the plenty of the new harvest of reform.

As was his habit, Emerson was considerably fair to these fanatics; he saw their mood as a sign of the times, and he

could pay tribute to disinterestedness. But in the end, he
condemns them for being "mechanical." Though the reformers always thought he should become one of them,
just as George Ripley assumed that he would join Brook
Farm, Emerson all his life fought not to let himself be dis-
tracted from the siege of his hen-coop to march off to a
pretended siege of Babylon. When they realized this, the
reformers came to hate him worse than they hated the conservatives of Back Bay; to them he became the arch-traitor.
But in his essay about them, quietly but devastatingly
showing wherein they had narrowed their minds and given
up to reform what was meant for the Over-Soul, he in-
sisted that the true advance of the age was a casting off of
material aids and "the indication of growing trust in the
private, self-supplied powers of the individual."

Remember that when he wrote these lines Emerson was
still considered by conservative Boston and by Harvard
College the radical of "The Divinity School Address." And
remember also that as he watched the industrialization of
New England he saw nothing beautiful in power looms;
he lamented that things were in the saddle and were riding
mankind. I agree, at once, that over the years Emerson
did not hold in strict consistency this individualistic
stance. Eventually, by the marriage of his daughter to a
Forbes, he too was incorporated into the web of wealth,
and in his last days was supported, as were Lowell and
Longfellow, by the proceeds of the Industrial Revolution.
In the course of time, his preaching of individualism, especially "self-reliance," came to seem not at all dangerous,
but rather the proper code for a young businessman with
get-up and go. It was discovered that Emerson could be
admitted to the placid manners of the Saturday Club,
which met in the Parker House. And after the Fugitive

Slave Act he did speak out against slavery so that, once the Civil War was finished, he could not be accused of having failed to do his part in the supreme among the New England crusades.

But these are pieces of Emerson's biography, not of the doctrine he promulgated, which in historical textbooks we call "Transcendentalism." As you know, the problem for the historian of defining Transcendentalism is virtually insurmountable because nobody at the time could define it, or rather no two Transcendentalists could agree on the same definition. Yet that it is there, and that it was an element in the intellectual configuration of the culture, this cannot be denied. And its importance is by no means diminished by the fact that the band of Transcendentalists was numerically very small, or that for years they were universally ridiculed by the Brahmin gentlemen, by the grubby reformers, and by the captains of New England industry. James Russell Lowell, William Lloyd Garrison, Nathan Appleton—to take these as symbolic figures—had one thing in common: they could despise Henry Thoreau.

For as we can see now, what was hard to see then, Thoreau made none of the concessions or compromises Emerson did. When Emerson once tried to get him to come a little way toward healing the breach with gentility, to attend a meeting of the Saturday Club, Thoreau replied that he went to Boston as little as possible, that when there, as soon as his business was done, the only room in all the city he wanted to visit was the men's room of the Fitchburg Station where he could wait for the train back to Concord. Nor do I need to read any of his by now famous indictments of the American absorption in business. If his target was not so clearly the factories and mills as it was the agricultural economy of his town, still it is clear that what he was orating against was the whole spirit of money-making. When he did for a moment turn his attention to those looms which Nathan Appleton had found beautiful, he perceived a beauty which might go far to explain Appleton's sense of the aesthetic:

> Where is this division of labor to end? and what object does it serve? I cannot believe that our factory system is the best model by which men may get clothing. The condition of the operatives is becoming every day more and more like that of the English; and it cannot be wondered at, since, as far as I have heard or observed, the principal object is, not that mankind may be well and honestly clad, but, unquestionably, that corporations may be enriched.

And as for reform, for doing good, for bettering the lot of his fellows, when he was told that his way of life was selfish, he could reply that he had no genius for charity, and that, "As for Doing-good, that is one of the professions which are full." In 1853 his mother's boarding house was suddenly infested with "three ultra-reformers," and Thoreau's pages on them are among his most vitriolic; he is disgusted with "the greasy cheeks of their kindness"; "They would not keep their distance, but cuddle up and lie spoon-fashion with you, no matter how hot the weather nor how narrow the bed." One of them so sought to convert Henry as though to take him into his bowels—"Men's bowels are far more slimy than their brains." This is about the nearest to a string of profanity Henry Thoreau ever came in his *Journal,* and here he did show the inveterate hostility of the true spirit of Transcendentalism to organized reform.

Again, all this is not a complete story. I am leaving out,

for instance, Emily Dickinson: she makes another and a longer lecture. And it is true that some Transcendentalists have links with Brahmin Boston: Dr. Holmes would write a life of Emerson. And many authentic Transcendentalists, like Parker and Ripley, got involved with some or another of the reforms. But, for the sake of clarifying our terms, Henry Thoreau is invaluable: Transcendentalism, he lets us see, was in essence a protest against the internal linkage of our other three actors. The fourth side of our parallelogram does not join at the corners, it breaks away. And yet it is as authentically of New England as the others, and because it was articulate it comes down as a principal, maybe *the* principal, heritage of nineteenth-century New England.

I think it evident on all sides, as time goes on, as our perspective of the New England terrain gains distance, that critical estimate of Thoreau proves him more and more the major writer of the Transcendental group, indeed of the period. This occasionally causes discomfort, to those who admire him no less than to the many who still dislike him and always will. If you toy with the question of what modern society might do with a reformer who denounces the Constitution as a Covenant with Hell, or with an ideologue who seizes a United States arsenal and starts shooting, what, you must ask, would it do with the author of "Civil Disobedience" and "Life Without Principle"? There really isn't anything you can say about him except that he is ultimate in subversion, because he would subvert even the reformers, let alone the conservatives. It is New England's Thoreau who still exhorts us: "If the law is of such a nature that it requires you to be an agent of injustice to another, then, I say, break the law. Let your life be a counter friction to stop the machine."

I leave you to settle with yourself how you shall take Henry Thoreau. To go back to our starting points, Barrett Wendell recognized Thoreau's craftsmanship in prose, but concluded that the constant obtrusion of his personality, his unflagging self-consciousness, make him an inferior writer; the best Wendell could say for *Walden* was that "it remains a vital bit of literature for any one who loves to read about Nature." Twenty-six years later, Parrington plays down the poet-naturalist, hails the social philosopher precisely for the extremes of individualism, calls his "one of the great names in American literature," and predicts (in 1926) that he is only beginning to come into his own.

This story would surely puzzle Thoreau's fellow-townsmen and his contemporaries. What of "his own" does a man have to come into who, upon getting a Harvard degree, does absolutely nothing with it—nothing, that is, that Concord village or Nathan Appleton could see? Assuredly we can say this much: New England made him, and New England gives him to us. Ghandi might admire him, but he is inconceivable outside New England. In the long run it may possibly be that if you want to enumerate what has descended to us from nineteenth-century New England, and you find it difficult to put a finger on any specific idea or literary influence, when you perceive that the Household Poets no longer inspire our poets, that the reforming spirit has evaporated, and that the Industrial Revolution has gone so far beyond its Yankee origins as to render any study of them a work of archaeology—it just may be that the one thing which you will find has most emphatically descended from that age, which is effectively present with us today, is the growing reputation of, and the inescapable challenge of, Henry Thoreau.